Literacy Puzzle Book

**Crosswords,
spello-grams,
word games …
and much more**

Charles Cripps

Literacy Puzzle Book 2
LL01315
ISBN 1 85503 341 0
© Charles Cripps
Illustrated by Anna Curtis
All rights reserved
First published 2001
Reprinted 2002, 2004

Permission to Photocopy

LDA, Duke Street, Wisbech, Cambs PE13 2AE
3195 Wilson Drive, Grand Rapids, MI 49544, USA

TEACHER'S NOTES

Rationale

The Word Level component of The National Literacy Strategy provides teachers with a clearly defined programme for the teaching of spelling regarding 'what' to teach, and 'when' to teach it. In both YR and Y1 the teaching of spelling is heavily geared to the teaching of phonics. But this is phonics for reading, which is not the same as phonics for spelling. Clearly, in the early developmental stages of spelling children are reproducing auditory images. The danger, however, is that many children become so dependent on this 'sounding out' strategy that they remain 'phonic spellers' throughout their schooling. These are also the children who experience difficulty in acquiring the necessary visual strategies that are expected by Y3 Term 1.

Obviously, children must be able to hear and discriminate letter sounds, but spelling cannot be caught simply by listening to the sounds in words because the nature of English spelling is such that we can have more than one spelling for the same sound. For spelling it is important that visual skills are promoted from as early as possible and it is for this reason that the puzzles in 'Literacy Puzzles Book 1' promote both the auditory and the visual aspects of the spelling system. In 'Literacy Puzzles Book 2' the puzzles focus more and more on the visual aspect of learning to spell.

By working through these books children will gradually build up a 'phonic map' of English. They will be made aware that in English the same sound can have different spellings (e.g. bed and said) and the same spelling can have different sounds (e.g. bone, gone and done).

Design of the books

Learning to spell must be seen as fun. These books are designed to help children enjoy playing with words and having fun with them. Each puzzle page is designed to enable the teacher to use it with the whole class, a group or with individual children, within or outside the Literacy Hour. The puzzles will also be a useful support for other spelling material based on the visual approach.

The pronunciation used in this material follows the system of the International Phonetic Alphabet (IPA) and is based on the pronunciation associated especially with southern England (sometimes called 'Received Pronunciation').

The mute 'r' is used in puzzles involving vowel phonemes. That is, the 'r' in 'work' is used as a single phoneme and not as two separate sounds.

When children are writing words they must be encouraged to write them from memory, thus promoting the 'look-cover-write-check' technique.

This book builds on the work in Book 1 and introduces more complex phonic structures. Thus the 'phonic map' becomes more and more extensive. The puzzles also incorporate the high frequency and most frequently occurring words listed for Y4 - Y5.

The table of contents outlines in detail the additional differing aspects of spelling. For example, prefixes, suffixes, contractions etc.

Finish the pattern.

	+ s	+ ed	+ ing
jump	jumps	jumped	jumping
	walks		
		turned	
			asking
follow			
	starts		
		opened	

Can you change these words?

Turn **low** into a bird   `owl`

Turn **war** into uncooked

Turn **lime** into a distance

Turn **ram** into part of the body

Turn **stop** into containers

Turn **send** into finishes

Turn **sent** into a bird's home

Turn **ring** into a smile

Turn **mate** into not wild

Turn **care** into a competition

Now try these.

k o w e

Pat ... up early

d p t o e p s

means not moving

e i s t r

Jo ... hard

n e k w o

to have stopped
sleeping

Can you decode these sentences? The vowels (a – e – i – o – u) are missing.

S*m tr**s v*ry h*rd t* l**rn h*s sp*ll*ngs.

D*d w*s *s*d t* c*m*ng h*m* *n th* tr**n.

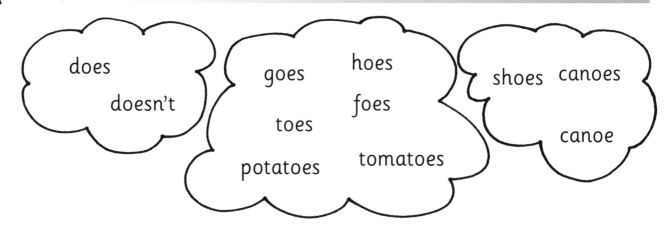

does
doesn't

goes
hoes
foes
toes
tomatoes
potatoes

shoes canoes
canoe

Write some of these words into a pattern shape below. Some shapes may be the same.

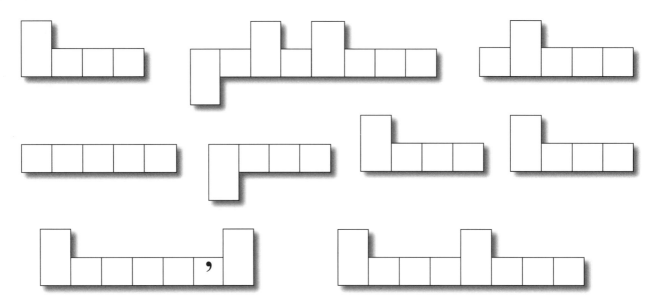

Begin at the top and find the eight words. The last letter of one word must always begin the next word.

Take away the ends of your feet and you can take it on the water.

n   e   c   e   t   o   a   s   o   [   ]

Can you find the **be** words in the word square? They are all horizontal.

l	o	b	e	f	o	r	e	d	r
u	b	e	f	b	e	g	a	n	e
p	b	e	i	n	g	i	n	g	s
b	e	n	b	e	l	o	w	s	e
s	e	b	e	t	w	e	e	n	d
b	e	l	o	n	g	i	n	d	g
f	o	r	b	e	n	e	a	t	h
a	b	e	s	i	d	e	d	o	n
e	b	i	b	e	h	i	n	d	e
o	b	e	c	a	u	s	e	s	s

....

....

....

....

....

....

....

....

....

Begin at the top and find the eight words. The last letter of one word must always begin the next word.

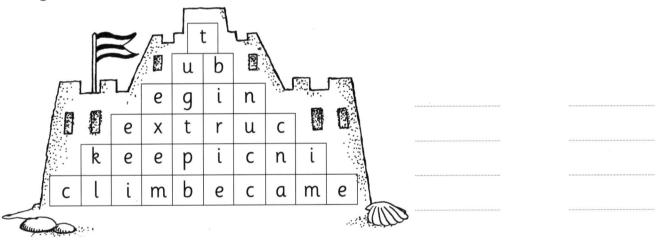

		t		
	u	b		
e	g	i	n	
e	x	t	r	u	c
k	e	e	p	i	c	n	i
c	l	i	m	b	e	c	a	m	e

....

....

....

This time write the eight words in the grid. The last letter of one word must always begin the next word.

		r		
	u	b		

become	not
tries	early
engine	sob
between	rub

Finish the puzzle by adding the pattern **igh** and most times a **t**.

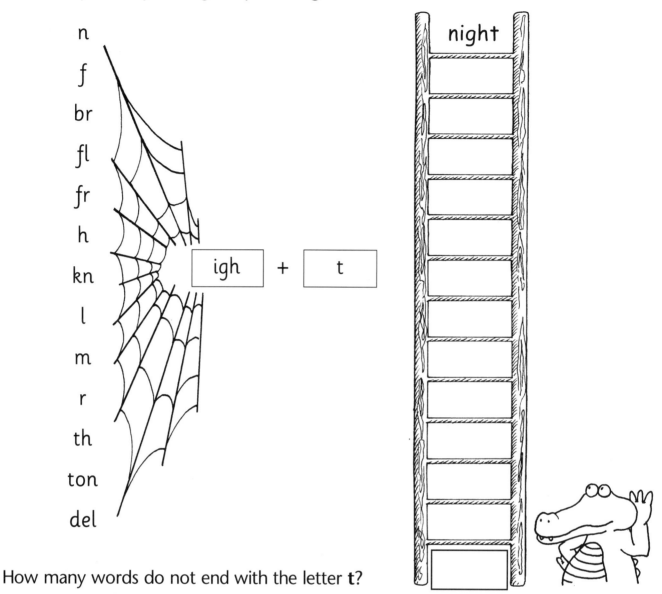

n

f

br

fl

fr

h

kn

l

m

r

th

ton

del

igh + t

night

How many words do not end with the letter **t**?

Can you turn **cats** into **mice** by changing each word one letter at a time?
There is a clue for each new word.

c	a	t	s

another word for tins

a stick to tie plants to

glass in a window

hair on a horse's neck

it's not yours but …

small furry animals

4

Begin with a silent **k** or a silent **w** to make new words.

not	rite	reck	now	neel

new	rap	nife	rote	nock

In these words the letters **ph** make the sound of an **f**.
Which word matches the clue? Fill in the missing letters.

trophy   sphere   graph   hyphen   phone   nephew

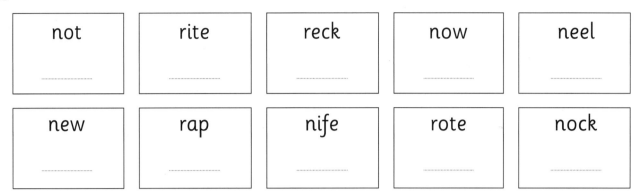

| p | h | | | it is round
| | | p | h | a chart
| | p | h | | joins two words

| p | h | | a mobile ...
| | p | h | | brother of niece
| | | p | h | the winner's prize

Can you finish the crosswords?

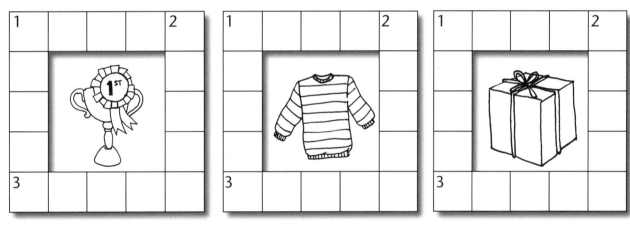

Across

1. used for cutting
3. Granny ... a pullover

Down

1. ... before entering
2. tests in school

Across

1. Lee ... a letter.
3. the day now

Down

1. part of your arm
2. opposite of full

Across

1. does up a parcel
3. a happening

Down

1. do it with a pen
2. opposite of stop

change	danger	strange	orange	angel	anger

Write each word into a pattern shape below.

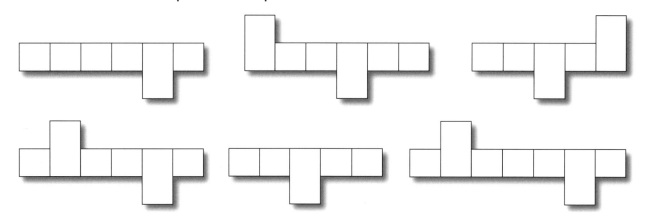

Use the words in the box to fill in the crossword.

changed	hanger
stranger	angels
anger	orange
change	danger
range	arrange

Finish the spello-gram.

My first is in **on** but not in **in**.

My second is in **hard** but not in **hand**.

My third is in **sand** but not in **send**.

My fourth is in **pine** but not in **pipe**.

My fifth is in **wage** but not in **wake**.

My sixth is in **east** but not in **past**.   What fruit am I?

Arrange these two word groups into alphabetical order.

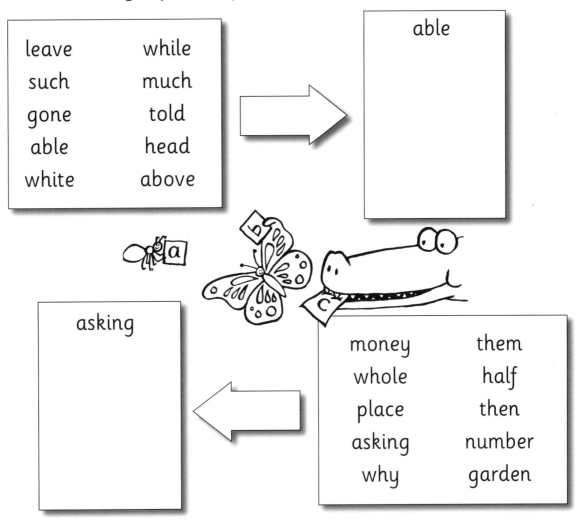

leave	while
such	much
gone	told
able	head
white	above

able

asking

money	them
whole	half
place	then
asking	number
why	garden

Arrange the words in alphabetical order in the correct column.

| flowers | pages | weeds | meat | story | lawn |
| cooking | words | biscuits | snails | titles | dinner |

Garden   **Books**   **Food**

Write these words in their own **ough** sound box.

though	cough	rough

bought   through   cough   bough   thought
drought   ought   though   rough   dough
brought   plough   borough   fought   enough
tough   although   nought   trough   sought
thorough

thorough	ought	bough

Which word needs a box of its own? [   ]

Write the sounds of each word in a box.

brought | b | r | ough | t |

fought [| |]

enough [| | |]

drought [| | |]

cough [| |]

though [|]

thought [| |]

rough [| |]

ought [|]

trough [| | |]

Can you find the **al** words in the word square? They are all vertical.

p	s	b	e	a	a	g	h	j	l	k	w
a	l	c	d	y	l	a	o	d	a	n	t
l	e	a	o	a	s	l	m	a	l	a	d
a	r	l	f	l	t	o	i	l	t	l	e
l	s	r	a	o	a	u	a	s	o	i	p
m	a	e	l	n	l	d	l	o	g	v	a
o	l	a	t	e	o	a	a	h	e	e	l
s	w	d	h	t	n	l	r	o	t	x	i
t	a	y	o	e	g	a	m	o	h	y	k
i	y	s	u	h	l	p	o	d	e	t	e
b	s	e	g	o	e	o	i	p	r	e	y
z	t	s	h	n	r	d	n	e	e	m	e

Begin at the top and find the eight words. The last letter of one word must always begin the next word.

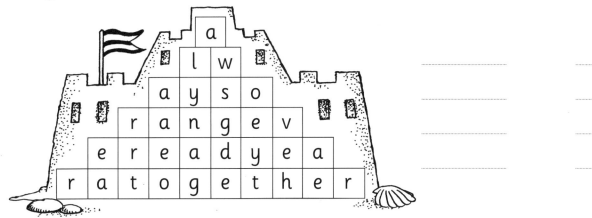

This time write the eight words in the grid. The last letter of one word must always begin the next word.

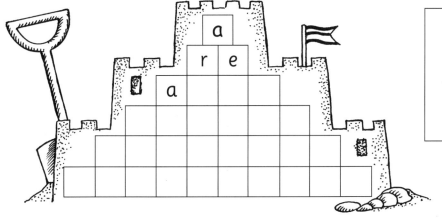

seventy	going
grew	area
ways	long
almost	tall

9

Make six **ever** and six **even** words.

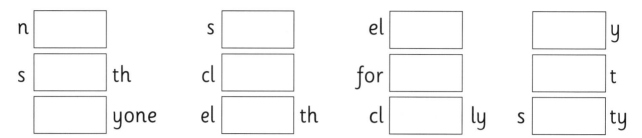

n ☐   s ☐   el ☐   ☐ y

s ☐ th   cl ☐   for ☐   ☐ t

☐ yone   el ☐ th   cl ☐ ly   s ☐ ty

Beginning with **c**, take every second letter to make eleven **ever** or **even** words. Write the words in the finishing box.

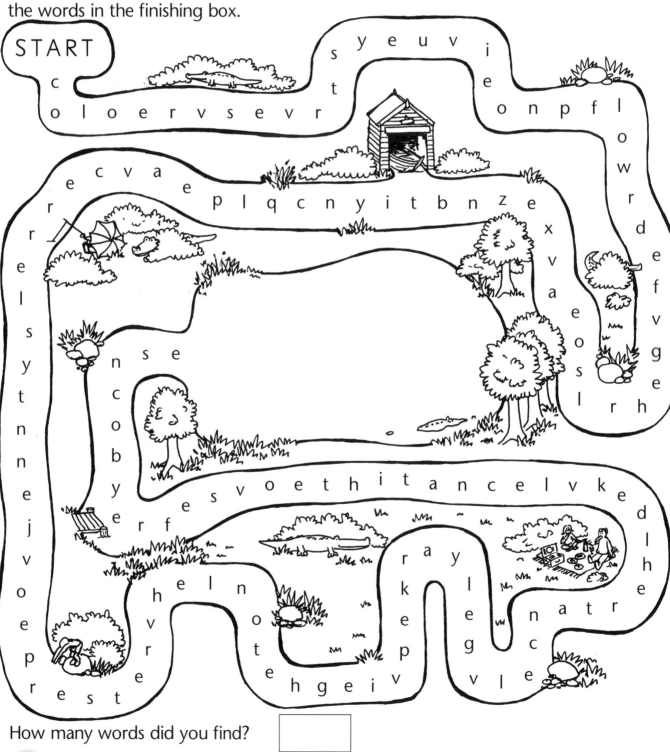

How many words did you find? ☐

Complete the words using the letters **on** or **un**.

		d	e	r
		l	y	
u	p			

		c	e
L		d		
		c	l	e

	f	r			t
			t	i	l
	p			y	

Write each **under** word into a pattern shape below. Some shapes may be the same.

| understand | understood | underneath | underline |

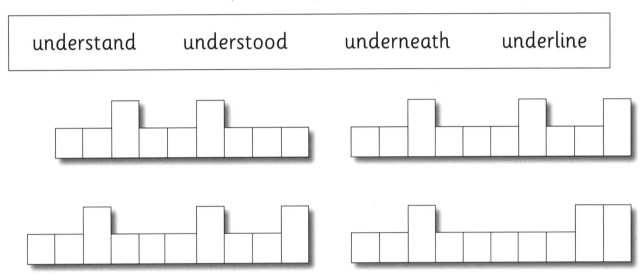

Finish the puzzles by printing under each letter the one that comes before it in the alphabet. Use capital letters.

T	O	J	G	G
N		T		S
B	O		H	P
S		U		O
U	S	P	V	U

V	O	E	F	S
Q		P		V
T	P		V	T
F		J		U
U	B	T	U	Z

Which word is the
opposite of back?

Which word is the
opposite of over?

Can you add these words together?

Beginning with **a**, take every second letter and write the five words in the finishing box.

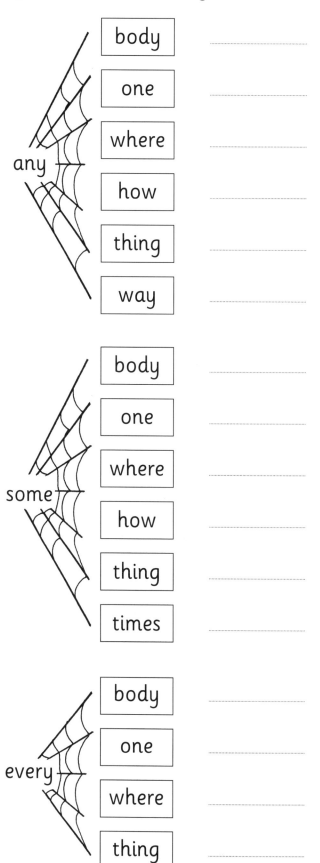

any
- body
- one
- where
- how
- thing
- way

some
- body
- one
- where
- how
- thing
- times

every
- body
- one
- where
- thing

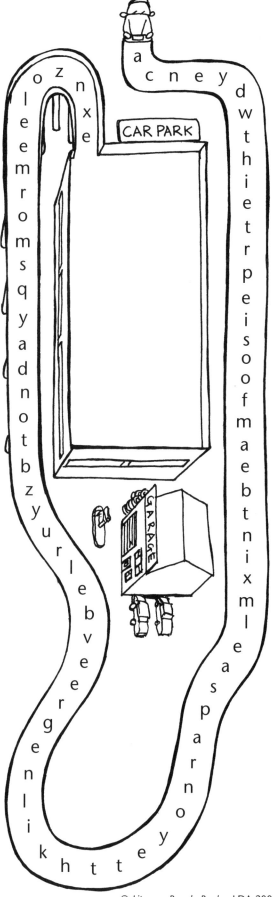

CAR PARK

GARAGE

Can you find the times of the day and the days in the word square?
They are all horizontal.

t	o	d	t	o	d	a	y	e	n	y
a	s	y	e	s	t	e	r	d	a	y
o	t	o	m	o	r	r	o	w	o	d
d	a	y	d	a	y	b	r	e	a	k
a	m	o	r	n	i	n	g	s	l	y
t	o	a	f	t	e	r	n	o	o	n
y	e	s	e	v	e	n	i	n	g	d
e	t	o	n	i	g	h	t	a	n	y
i	n	m	i	d	n	i	g	h	t	e
o	m	i	d	d	a	y	e	s	t	y

Write in the answers to finish the crossword.

3 letters   day

4 letters   year easy been

5 letters   today white weeks irons

6 letters   taking letter breeze

7 letters   tonight teacake

8 letters   earnings

10 letters   thoughtful

Write down the ten **ring** words hidden in the
word square. The words go across and down.

r	s	a	d	m	i	r	i	n	g
i	c	c	a	r	o	n	g	e	d
n	o	b	d	u	r	i	n	g	s
o	r	o	k	d	e	n	t	l	e
f	i	r	o	d	a	r	i	n	g
f	n	i	b	a	c	k	r	e	d
i	g	n	s	c	a	r	i	n	g
r	m	g	l	a	r	i	n	g	l
i	e	t	s	l	i	n	g	r	i
n	b	c	s	o	n	e	y	o	z
g	u	p	a	n	g	e	s	t	e

....

....

....

....

....

Write out the coded words.

a	1
b	2
c	3
d	4
e	5
f	6
g	7
h	8
i	9
j	10
k	11
l	12
m	13
n	14
o	15
p	16
q	17
r	18
s	19
t	20
u	21
v	22
w	23
x	24
y	25
z	26

4	21	18	9	14	7

2	15	18	9	14	7

3	1	18	9	14	7

19	3	15	18	9	14	7

4	1	18	9	14	7

1	4	13	9	18	9	14	7

7	12	1	18	9	14	7

6	9	18	9	14	7

19	3	1	18	9	14	7

20	9	18	9	14	7

Finish the sums.

s + oft = [   ]   oft + en = [   ]

l + oft = [   ]   s + oft + ly = [   ]

s + oft + en = [   ]   al + oft = [   ]

Finish the puzzle.

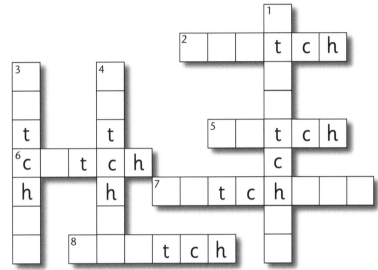

1.   often used for carrying a sick person
2.   you may need one if you break your leg
3.   a person who sells meat
4.   the room in the house used for cooking
5.   usually worn on the wrist
6.   Sam caught the first ball. Cathy will … the next one.
7.   a man from the Netherlands
8.   when you grab something quickly you …

Take away the opposite of **hard** and you are left with a teller of time.

   [   ]

Take away **frequently** and you can cook a meal here.

   [   ]

Use the code to find out the words.

a	b	c	d	e	f	g	h	i	j	k	l	m
Z	Y	X	W	V	U	T	S	R	Q	P	O	N

n	o	p	q	r	s	t	u	v	w	x	y	z
M	L	K	J	I	H	G	F	E	D	C	B	A

| Y | V | G | G | V | I |

| H | G | R | O | O |

| S | Z | K | K | B |

| W | R | U | U | V | I | V | M | G |

| H | F | W | W | V | M | O | B |

| H | D | R | N | N | R | M | T |

| Y | Z | O | O | L | L | M |

Use the words in the box
to fill in the crossword.

happiness	rabbit
winner	bigger
better	manner
sudden	hidden
swimming	error

Can you decode these sentences? The double consonant letters are missing.

Rebe**a was a be**er swi**er than her bi**er brother.

The shape of the blue ba**oon was sti** di**erent from the red one.

Su**enly, E**ie sto**ed crying and was ha**y again.

Finish the pattern. We add **er** when comparing two and **est** for more than two.

	+ er	+ est
fast	faster	fastest
great		
	nearer	
		roundest
small		
	louder	
		youngest

Now try these tricky ones. The base word changes.

little	less	least
good		
	more	
bad		

These numbers represent letters. Can you write the words?

1	2	3	4	5
s	t	a	l	e

5	3	1	2

4	3	1	2

4	5	1	1

2	3	4	5

1	5	4	4

1	5	3	2

1	2	5	3	4

4	5	3	1	2

Which word is a story?

| inside | outside | beside | sideways |
| without | outdoors | outline | outwards |

Write each word into a pattern shape below.

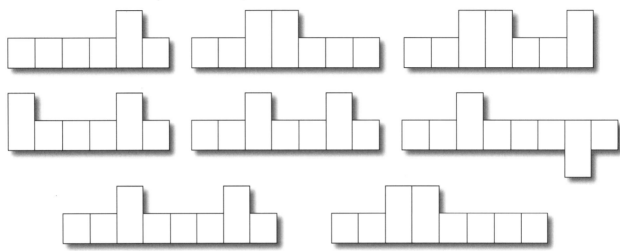

Now use some of the words to describe the pictures.

_ _ _ _ _ _

_ _ _ _ _ _ _

_ _ _ _ _ _

_ _ _ _ _ _

_ _ _ _ _ _

_ _ _ _ _ _ _

Can you decode these sentences? The vowels (a – e – i – o – u) are missing.

S*m* ch*ldr*n w*r* *ns*de *nd *th*rs w*r* **ts*d*.

T*d*y **r t**ch*r s**d w* c**ld pl*y **td**rs.

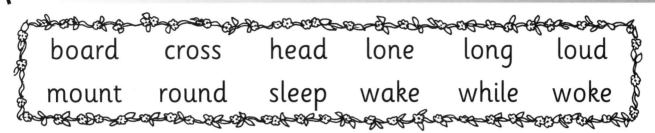

| board | cross | head | lone | long | loud |
| mount | round | sleep | wake | while | woke |

Write each word into a pattern shape below. Some shapes may be the same.

Then write each new word beginning with an **a**.

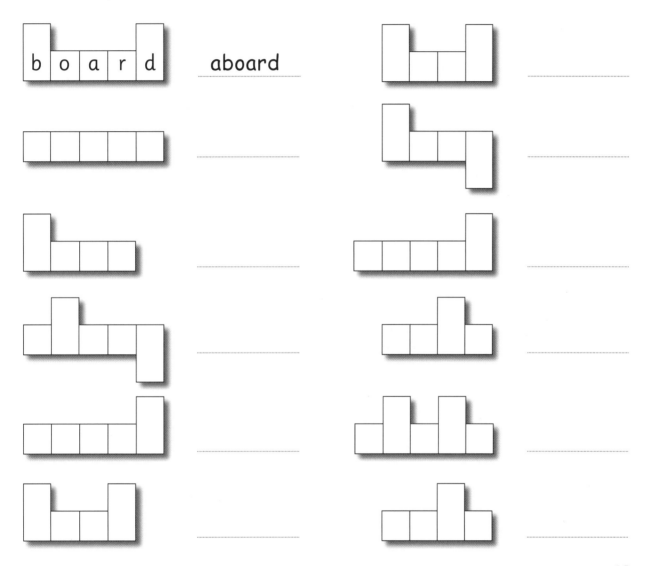

| b | o | a | r | d |

aboard

Can you decode these sentences? The vowels (a – e – i – o – u) are missing.

R∗j w∗∗t∗d ∗r∗∗nd th∗ c∗rn∗r ∗nt∗l h∗s fr∗∗nd c∗m∗ ∗l∗ng.

Th∗ sch∗∗l f∗t∗ r∗∗s∗d th∗ ∗m∗∗nt ∗f £500 f∗r ∗ n∗w c∗mp∗t∗r.

Find the **ath**, **eth** and **oth** words in the word square. They are all vertical.

e	l	y	s	o	r	c	f	b	i	t
m	g	e	o	f	o	a	i	i	b	o
o	a	t	t	a	b	l	l	g	o	f
t	r	o	h	t	r	t	c	a	t	a
h	a	g	e	h	o	o	l	t	b	t
e	t	e	r	p	t	g	o	h	o	h
r	h	t	l	a	h	e	t	e	t	e
e	e	h	o	t	e	t	h	r	h	r
d	r	e	b	h	r	h	e	e	o	a
s	e	r	o	e	i	e	s	f	r	n
a	y	n	t	p	s	r	t	d	g	e

Write in the answers to finish the crossword.

3 letters ape

4 letters both help path

5 letters above other truth froth tasty

6 letters trench bother

7 letters clothes scamper

8 letters takeaway

10 letters altogether

Change one letter in each word to spell the name of an animal.

big	deck	for	rut	cot	worse
....	....	....	....	....	....

Find the animals in the word square. They are all horizontal.

p	u	d	p	u	p	p	i	e	s	s
a	n	g	l	l	i	o	n	e	s	t
s	a	l	e	o	p	a	r	d	e	d
j	i	r	a	g	i	r	a	f	f	e
c	a	k	i	t	t	e	n	s	n	y
d	o	n	t	m	o	n	k	e	y	y
a	r	r	e	i	n	d	e	e	r	k
h	a	r	h	o	r	s	e	t	o	e
c	o	t	i	g	e	r	e	s	e	n
a	d	o	n	k	e	y	t	i	o	n

....

....

....

....

....

....

....

....

....

....

Use the animal words in the box to fill in the crossword.

animals	kitten
giraffe	tiger
monkey	horse
leopard	dog

Take away the parent of a foal and you are left with a tall animal.

r   s   f   h   a   r   g   f   o   i   e   e   [   ]

Sort out the jumbled letters into two words. Then turn them into contractions. Do not forget the apostrophe.

tonidd	=	didn't	rtonae	=	
nacton	=		tonsaw	=	
dtono	=		adtonh	=	
stonha	=		vetonha	=	
stoni	=		retonwe	=	
cuotonld	=		wtonuodl	=	
houtonsdl	=		siti	=	
siereht	=		hatsit	=	
erehis	=		reayuo	=	
mIa	=		avehI	=	

Finish the crossword by using the contraction of each clue. Use a separate square for each apostrophe.

Across
2. would not
6. is not
7. I am
8. did not
9. she will

Down
1. do not
3. does not
4. that is
5. cannot
7. I will

Finish the **ound** puzzle.

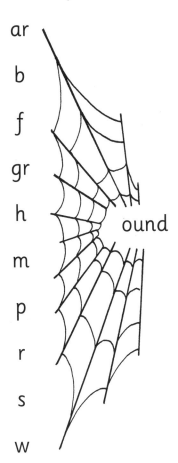

ar
b
f
gr
h   ound
m
p
r
s
w

	+	ing	=
	+	ed	=
	+	ed	=
	+	s	=
	+	s	=
	+	ed	=
	+	er	=
	+	ing	=

Can you finish the rhyming crossword?

Across

1. rhymes with sound
3. rhymes with bought
6. rhymes with train
7. rhymes with page
9. rhymes with rough
10. rhymes with mound

Down

2. rhymes with brown
4. rhymes with caught
5. rhymes with tree
7. rhymes with dish
8. rhymes with mutter

Can you find the **ear** words?

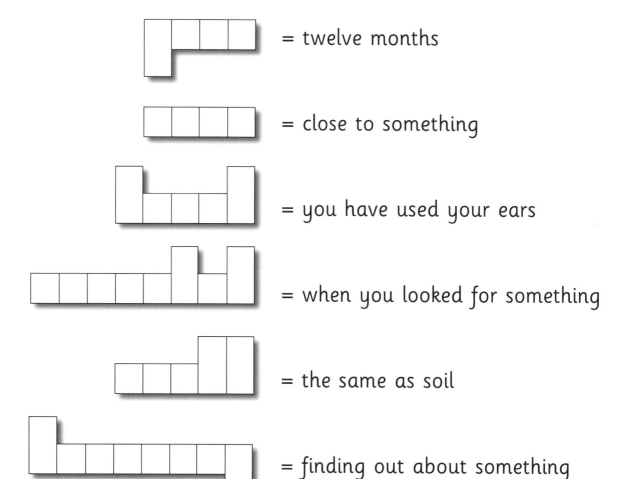

= twelve months

= close to something

= you have used your ears

= when you looked for something

= the same as soil

= finding out about something

Can you decode these sentences? The vowels (a – e – i – o – u) are missing.

N∗xt y∗∗r w∗ w∗ll b∗ tr∗nsf∗rr∗ng t∗ ∗∗r n∗w sch∗∗l.

∗t ∗∗r n∗w sch∗∗l w∗ w∗ll b∗g∗n t∗ l∗∗rn Fr∗nch.

Th∗ s∗∗rch f∗r th∗ l∗st d∗g h∗d l∗st∗d tw∗ d∗ys.

Th∗ s∗∗rch∗rs f∗∗nd th∗ d∗g wh∗n th∗y h∗∗rd ∗ts cr∗∗s f∗r h∗lp.

Can you find the members of the family? The words are all horizontal.

a	s	i	s	i	s	t	e	r	l	e
g	r	o	n	d	f	a	t	h	e	r
f	e	u	n	c	l	e	s	t	l	y
a	n	b	r	o	t	h	e	r	e	r
f	e	h	a	u	n	t	e	i	n	g
p	o	n	n	e	p	h	e	w	c	y
u	n	c	l	a	u	n	t	i	e	d
a	m	o	t	h	e	r	s	a	n	t
t	o	c	o	u	s	i	n	e	n	d
b	a	b	b	a	b	y	l	t	e	x
a	c	h	i	l	d	r	e	n	e	l
s	i	s	b	e	n	i	e	c	e	r

Begin at the top and find the eight words. The last letter of one word must always begin the next word.

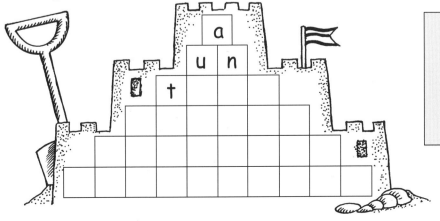

Within the castle:
```
        c
      o   u
    s   i   n   i
  e   c   e   m   u   n
c   l   e   l   f   a   t   h
e   r   a   i   n   e   p   h   e   w
```

This time write the eight words in the grid. The last letter of one word must always begin the next word.

Castle grid letters shown: a / u n / t

aunt	sister
sun	yes
baby	tub
relations	nephew

Join each word in the box with a word below to make compound words.

Only use each word once.

after	day	news	for	bed	out
birth	card	post	fire	dish	door

____cloth	____light	____noon
____side	____board	____day
____knob	____room	____paper
____box	____ward	____place

Use each consonant once to finish some of the compound words above.

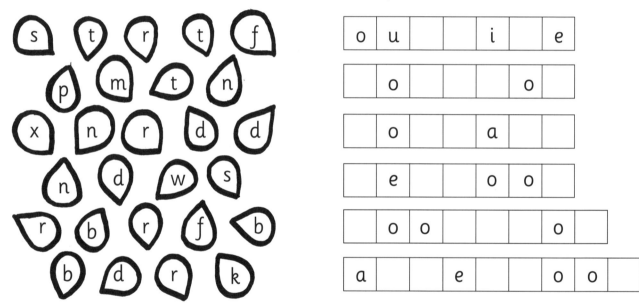

s	t	r	t	f

| p | m | t | n |

| x | n | r | d | d |

| n | d | w | s |

| r | b | r | f | b |

| b | d | r | k |

o	u			i		e

| | o | | | | o | |

| | o | | a | | |

| | e | | | o | o |

| | o | o | | | | o | |

| a | | | e | | | o | o | |

The beginning words have the wrong endings. Can you sort them out?

dish	noon		
in	light		
snow	case		
news	cloth		

dish	cloth		

flower	ball		
after	paper		
head	side		
stair	bed		

Write each **ure** word and draw a line to its meaning.

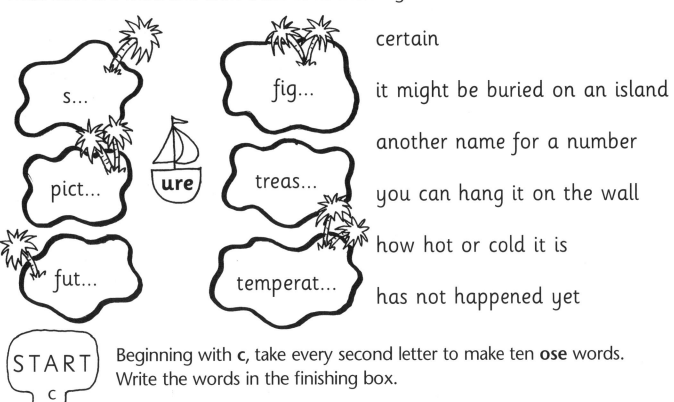

certain

it might be buried on an island

another name for a number

you can hang it on the wall

how hot or cold it is

has not happened yet

s...

pict...

fut...

fig...

treas...

temperat...

ure

START Beginning with **c**, take every second letter to make ten **ose** words.
Write the words in the finishing box.

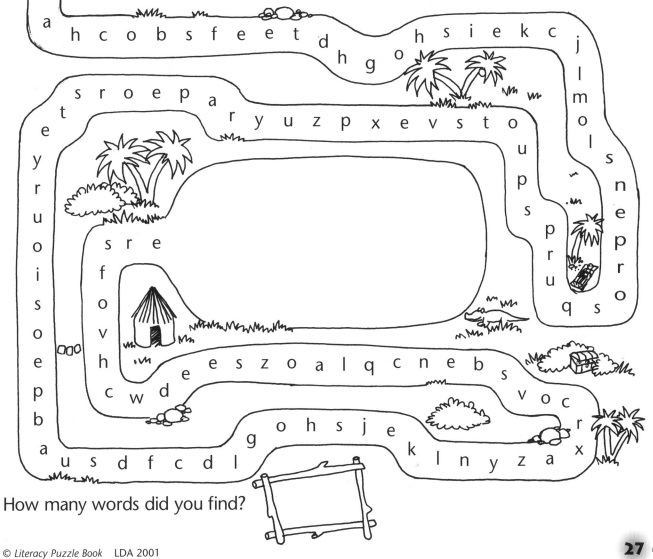

How many words did you find?

Take a word from the box and write it beside its opposite in the lake.

after	back
here	last
little	many
right	push
taken	never

	always			there
	few			before
	big			first
	given			front
	wrong			pull

Now try some more. The opposites are under the tree.

	same			sold
	lost			over
	black			stopped
	shut			old
	below			outside

above	different
bought	started
found	under
inside	white
open	young

These answers have been put in the wrong boxes. Can you correct them?

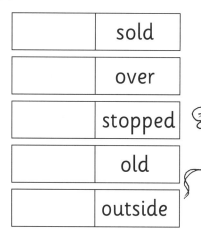

The opposite of bottom is ... | wrong | | |

The opposite of question is ... | heavy | | |

The opposite of correct is ... | north | | |

The opposite of light is ... | top | | |

The opposite of south is ... | sell | | |

The opposite of buy is ... | answer | | |

Make six **port** words and six **light** words.

s ☐   f ☐   s ☐ ly   im ☐ ant

re ☐   de ☐   ☐ rait   ☐ ning

☐ ing   ☐ hole   ☐ able   ☐ en

Can you find the two hidden words? Take every second letter in a clockwise direction. Go around the lifebelt twice and write the words in the centre.

Start here

Find the smaller words in each long word. Can you find them all?

heart	he a hear ear art	5
thinking		8
shown		5
disappear		8
everywhere		8
discovery		7
important		8
something		7
interesting		8
stranger		8

Finish the puzzles by printing under each letter the one that comes before it in the alphabet. Use capital letters.

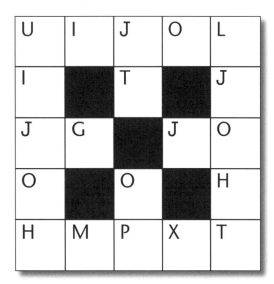

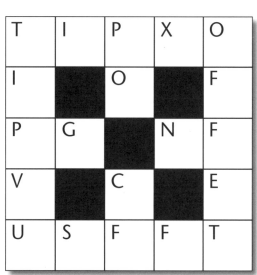

Which word means
shines with steady light?

Which word means
say something loudly?

Beginning with **w**, take every second letter to make twelve **wor** words.
Write the words in the finishing box.

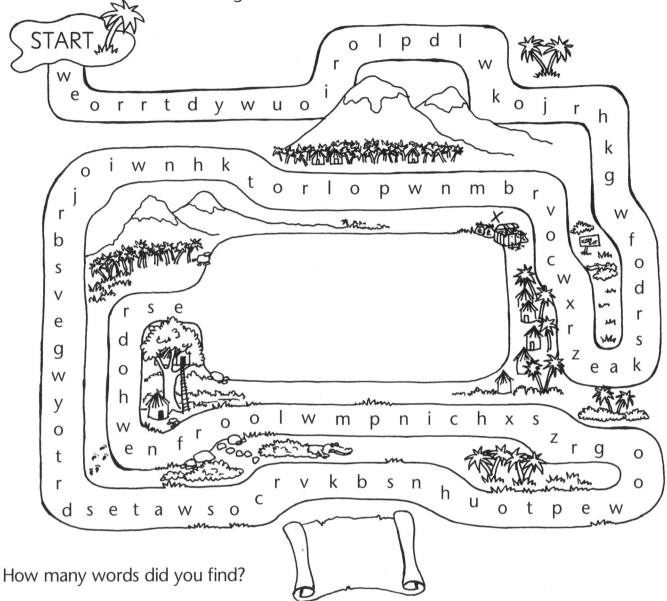

How many words did you find?

Subtract a letter from each word in the first column. The clues will help you to find the new word. Use the subtracted letters to find the opposite of **best**.

Words	Clues	Word	Letter
town	a very heavy weight		
point	a measure of liquid		
work	used for cooking		
worse	Jenny ... her black boots		
trip	a tear in your coat		

The opposite of **best** is ☐

Make four **ape**, four **wind** and four **end** words.

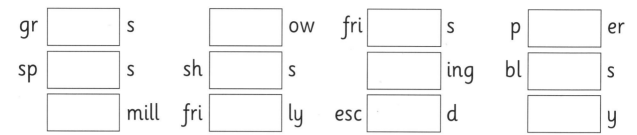

gr ☐ s   ☐ ow   fri ☐ s   p ☐ er

sp ☐ s   sh ☐ s   ☐ ing   bl ☐ s

☐ mill   fri ☐ ly   esc ☐ d   ☐ y

Look at the letters in each shape and finish the puzzle.

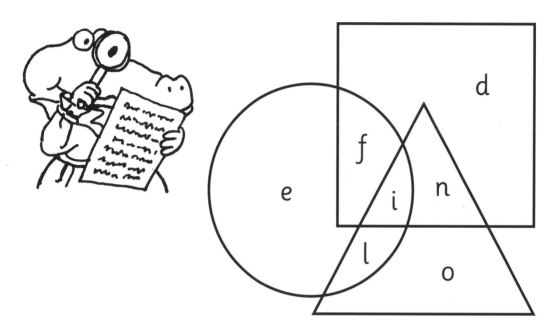

Which letter appears only in the circle?   ☐

Which two letters appear in the square and the triangle?   ☐ ☐

Which letter appears only in the square?   ☐

What word can you spell with these four letters?   ☐

Which letter appears in all three shapes?   ☐

What word can you make with the four letters in the square?   ☐

What two letters do you need to turn this word into **friend**?   ☐ ☐

Can you make two words with the letters in the circle?   ☐ ☐

What animal can you make with the four letters in the triangle?   ☐

Finish the patterns.

one	more than one
animal	
eye	
house	
place	

one	more than one
box	
glass	
bush	
watch	

one	more than one
fly	
spy	
lady	
baby	

one	more than one
half	
calf	
knife	
wife	

one	more than one
echo	
hero	
potato	
tomato	

Be careful with these patterns.

one	more than one
child	
foot	
tooth	
mouse	

one	more than one
deer	
sheep	
trout	
cod	

Finish the spello-gram.

My first is in **calf** but not in **half**.
My second is in **halves** but not in **calves**.
My third is in **write** but not in **wrote**.
My fourth is in **flies** but not in **fries**.
My fifth is in **cod** but not in **cot**.
My sixth is in **deer** but not in **deep**.
My seventh is in **one** but not in **won**.
My eighth is in **nice** but not in **mice**.   Who are we?

These words have the same sound but different spellings.

a large animal

uncovered

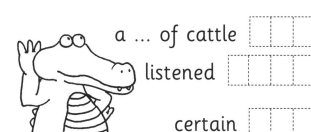

a ... of cattle

listened

certain

the coastline

not wrong

use a pen to ...

have on as clothing

to what place

a colour

the wind ...

the opposite of yes

I ... the way

sports day was ...

make tiny pieces

he ... the ball

end to end

you can dig one

all of something

Cross out all the letters that appear twice in each grid below.
Then rearrange the remaining letters to give the two homophones.

e	f	i	a	z	b
y	t	v	l	n	x
c	k	p	j	d	s
x	h	a	s	y	o
z	l	b	i	k	c
d	v	j	r	p	f

Answer _____

c	i	a	s	d	o
g	f	l	i	y	v
m	h	z	w	p	b
b	n	u	g	v	z
d	s	y	p	c	t
f	r	u	a	m	l

Answer _____

Make six **eye** and six **lad** words.

	s			y		ies		ball
g				lid		brow	g		ly
	lash	b		e		sight	sa	

Four of these words are hidden in the circle below. Take every second letter and go clockwise around the eye twice. Write the words in the centre.

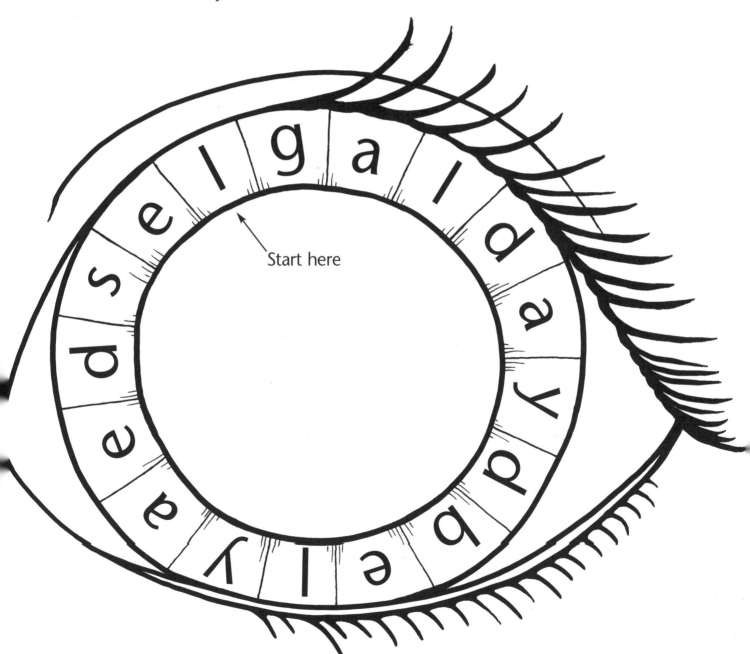

Start here

Decode each jumbled young animal and use it to finish the clues below.

tnetki	bmla	lickudgn	idk	gnilosg	glipet
kitten					

lepodta	lafc	ucb	loaf	gycten	upp

A young dog is called a ☐   A young bear is called a ☐

A young cow is called a ☐   A young duck is called a ☐

A young sheep is called a ☐   A young frog is called a ☐

A young swan is called a ☐   A young horse is called a ☐

A young goose is called a ☐   A young pig is called a ☐

A young goat is called a ☐   A young cat is called a ☐

These answers have been put in the wrong boxes. Can you correct them?

hutch	den
den	
web	
nest	
burrow	
kennel	
stable	
form	
shell	
hive	

The home of a lion is called a …

A bee lives in a …

The home of a bird is called a …

A dog lives in a …

The home of a horse is called a …

The home of a tame rabbit is called a …

A wild rabbit lives in a …

The home of a spider is called a …

The home of a hare is called a …

A snail lives in a …

Decode each word and use it to finish the clues below.

a	b	c	d	e	f	g	h	i	j	k	l	m
Z	Y	X	W	V	U	T	S	R	Q	P	O	N

n	o	p	q	r	s	t	u	v	w	x	y	z
M	L	K	J	I	H	G	F	E	D	C	B	A

| Y | Z | O | V | | S | V | I | W | | X | I | V | D | | U | O | L | X | P |

| T | Z | T | T | O | V | | X | S | V | H | G | | H | D | Z | I | N |

| H | X | S | L | L | O | | Y | F | M | X | S | | G | I | L | L | K |

| O | R | G | G | V | I | | Y | L | F | J | F | V | G |

a [   ] of sailors   a [   ] of flowers

a [   ] of birds   a [   ] of grapes

a [   ] of geese   a [   ] of drawers

a [   ] of cattle   a [   ] of whales

a [   ] of pups   a [   ] of bees

a [   ] of wool   a [   ] of monkeys

Take away the ship's crew and you are left with the fruit.

r   i   p   s   a   r   s   a   s   g   l   e   o   [   ]

Take away the young dogs and you have somewhere to put your clothes.

s   p   a   u   p   d   e   r   p   s   i   w   r   e   [   ]

Decode each jumbled word and use it to finish the clues below.

korc	wol	blam	heratef	linsa	nebo
rock					

suome	ebe	reah	stohg	rebmuccu	nilo

as brave as a ...   [ ]   as slow as a ...   [ ]

as busy as a ...   [ ]   as wise as an ...   [ ]

as fast as a ...   [ ]   as white as a ...   [ ]

as cool as a ...   [ ]   as dry as a ...   [ ]

as gentle as a ...   [ ]   as light as a ...   [ ]

as quiet as a ...   [ ]   as steady as a ...   [ ]

Who does what? The answers are all wrong. Can you correct them?

A person who mends pipes and taps is a ... | florist | [ ]

A person who looks after our teeth is a ... | jockey | [ ]

A person who looks after our eyes is an ... | pilot | [ ]

A person who grows plants is a ... | plumber | [ ]

A person who rides a race horse is a ... | butcher | [ ]

A person who flies an aeroplane is a ... | optician | [ ]

A person who makes us laugh at the circus is a ... | gardener | [ ]

A person who sells flowers is a ... | artist | [ ]

A person who sells meat is a ... | dentist | [ ]

A person who paints pictures is an ... | clown | [ ]

Each sentence is wrong. Can you write the correct animal in the boxes?

a **pig** neighs and gallops

a **horse** barks and runs

a **mouse** brays and trots

a **duck** roars and prowls

a **dog** squeaks and scampers

a **lion** talks and walks

a **bird** grunts and trots

a **hen** whistles and flies

a **donkey** quacks and waddles

a **turkey** cackles and struts

a **elephant** gobbles and struts

an **person** trumpets and ambles

Use each vowel below to finish the animals.

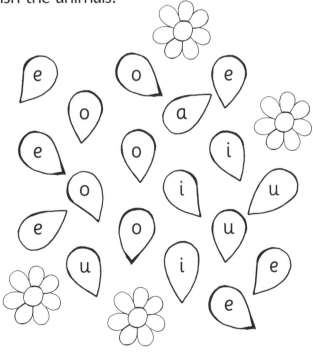

p		g		
d		g		
b		r	d	
d		c	k	
l			n	
m			s	
h		r	s	
d		n	k	y
t		r	k	y
	l		p	h	n	t

Decode each jumbled word and use it to finish the proverbs below.

reven	lemi	tonreha	tarped	edinde	enin
never					

nidm	kilea	pela	lewl	tegrheot	wens

A fool and his money are soon ...

A friend in need is a friend ...

All's well that ends ...

A miss is as good as a ...

A stitch in time saves ...

Better late than ...

Birds of a feather flock ...

Great minds think ...

Look before you ...

No news is good ...

One good turn deserves ...

Out of sight, out of ...

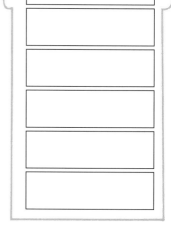

Can you decode these proverbs? Every word is jumbled.

A tichst ni meti avess enin.   sdriB fo a thefear lfokc otertheg.

_____   _____

A endirf ni deen si a firdne nedide.   tteBer tale anth veern.

_____   _____

Use these words to finish the puzzles below.

painting	modern	south	army	fish	month
nephew	leg	up	April	mother	woman

boy is to man as girl is to ...

father is to son as ... is to daughter

high is to low as ... is to down

wrist is to arm as ankle is to ...

north is to ... as east is to west

uncle is to ... as aunt is to niece

wing is to bird as fin is to ...

June is to July as ... is to May

day is to week as ... is to year

rich is to poor as ancient is to ...

soldier is to ... as sailor is to navy

artist is to ... as author is to writing

Begin at the top and find the eight words. The last letter of one word must always begin the next word.

```
            w
          o   m
        a  n  e  p
      h  e  w  h  y  o
    u  n  g  h  o  s  t  o
  o  n  i  o  n  s  o  u  t  h
```

Can you answer the puzzles?

What day comes before Tuesday?

What day comes after Saturday?

What day is between Tuesday and Thursday?

Write the word for the number of days in a week.

What day is two days before Sunday?

What day is between Monday and Wednesday?

MARCH

1	2	3	4	5	6	7
8	9	10	11	12	13	14
15	16	17	18	19	20	21
22	23	24	25	26	27	28
29	30	31				

What day is between Friday and Sunday?

What is the abbreviation for Wednesday?

How many days are there in a fortnight?

How many days start with the letter 'T'?

What day is two days after Tuesday?

How many days are there in a leap year?

Finish the sentences. Each dash stands for a letter.

Last T_ _ _ _ day it was very hot, but F_ _ day was cold and wet.

We will be in Scotland from next Wed_ _ _ day to Sat_ _day.

This year my birthday is on a M_ _day.

Can you come over to my
house next T_ _ _ day?

What month am I?

Abbreviations of the months begin with capital letters and end with full stops.
May, **June** and **July** are not abbreviated.

Jan.	January	**July**	July
Feb.		**Aug.**	
Mar.		**Sept.**	
Apr.		**Oct.**	
May		**Nov.**	
June		**Dec.**	

Finish the spello-gram.

What month am I?

My first letter is in **fit** but not in **bit**.
My second letter is in **well** but not in **wall**.
My third letter is in **tube** but not in **tune**.
My fourth letter is in **read** but not in **bead**.
My fifth letter is in **aunt** but not in **ant**.
My sixth letter is in **lake** but not in **like**.
My seventh letter is in **crown** but not in **clown**.
My eighth letter is in **by** but not in **be**.

I am the month of _____.

Fill in the missing words.

Thirty days hath S_____, A_____, J_____ and N_____.
All the rest have _____, excepting F_____ all alone, which
has but _____ days clear, and _____ in each leap year.

Finish the pattern.

1	one	1st	11	eleven	11th
			13		
3					
			15		
5					
			17		
7					
			19		
9					

Can you do these number puzzles? Write your answers in words.

What comes between twelve and fourteen?

How many less than nineteen is ten?

Take eight from nine and add eleven.

Add five, seven and eight.

What is half of two less than sixteen?

Multiply four by four.

How many articles in a dozen?

Divide eighteen by six.

What is the second even number after ten?

What is the third odd number after ten?

These answers have been put in the wrong boxes. Can you correct them?

Question	Answer	Correct
What is nine more than twenty?	88	
What is 99 in words?	29	
What comes between sixty-nine and seventy-one?	59	
Add twenty-four and twelve.	30	
Multiply six by eight.	70	
What number comes just before sixty?	24	
What is eleven more than seventy-seven?	36	
How many is two dozen?	40	
Take twenty from fifty.	100	
What number comes next after thirty-nine?	89	
What is two before ninety-one?	48	
How many is a century?	ninety-nine	

Which numbers are we mixing?

t y e w n	d e r n u d	y t r i h
t_____	h_____	t_____

o y t r	e i y n t	n e v t e y
f_____	n_____	s_____

t h g i y	x y i t	i y t f
e_____	s_____	f_____

Which colours are we mixing?

mix yellow and [ ] to make green

mix blue and [ ] to make purple

mix red and [ ] to make orange

mix black and [ ] to make grey

mix blue and red to make [ ]

mix blue and yellow to make [ ]

mix black and white to make [ ]

mix red and yellow to make [ ]

mix red and white to make [ ]

mix red and green to make   br _ _ _

Cross out all the letters that appear twice in each grid below. Then rearrange the remaining letters to give the names of two colours.

c	u	a	o	k	e
f	l	t	h	r	v
m	b	p	f	o	d
e	v	y	a	g	h
t	n	r	l	u	c
d	y	b	i	g	m

d	b	w	u	k	e
s	o	z	f	x	j
n	p	h	y	c	s
j	v	x	y	a	z
f	c	r	b	u	p
h	w	k	g	d	v

Answer _____

Answer _____

Name and draw a line to the parts of the body.

foot   leg   wrist   neck   eye

toe   knee   hand   mouth   nose

head   tongue   shoulder   finger   shin

hair   ear   elbow   thigh   ankle

Sometimes words in our language have the same spelling but different sounds and meanings. These words are called heteronyms.

Finish these sentences by using the word pairs.

wound	wound	produce	produce	refuse	refuse
present	present	row	row	minute	minute
close	close	wind	wind	tear	tear

When Sara saw the _____ in her new coat she shed a _____ .

The tables were too _____ for him to _____ the door.

The bandage was _____ around the _____ to stop it bleeding.

The tip was so full that the Council had to _____ more _____ .

The _____ was so strong the sailors had to _____ in the sails.

The farmer worked hard to _____ as much _____ as possible.

The children were ready to _____ the headteacher with her leaving _____ .

Every _____ there seemed to be a _____ musical sound from the computer.

There was a _____ among the crew about the best way to _____ .

Here are some more funny ones to answer.

Is a kiwifruit a bird?	yes/no
Do you have ham in hamburgers?	yes/no
Are boxing rings round?	yes/no
One tooth, two teeth. Is the plural of booth, beeth?	yes/no
One goose, two geese. Is the plural of moose, meese?	yes/no

PUZZLE 1 — Words ending with the suffixes s, ed and ing

Finish the pattern.

	+ s	+ ed	+ ing
jump	jumps	jumped	jumping
walk	walks	walked	walking
turn	turns	turned	turning
ask	asks	asked	asking
follow	follows	followed	following
start	starts	started	starting
open	opens	opened	opening

Can you change these words?

Now try these.

Turn **low** into a bird — owl

k o w e
Pat ... up early
woke

Turn **war** into uncooked — raw

Turn **lime** into a distance — mile

d p t o e p s
means not moving
stopped

Turn **ram** into part of the body — arm

Turn **stop** into containers — pots

Turn **send** into finishes — ends

e i s t r
Jo ... hard
tries

Turn **sent** into a bird's home — nest

Turn **ring** into a smile — grin

n e k w o
to have stopped
sleeping
woken

Turn **mate** into not wild — tame

Turn **care** into a competition — race

Can you decode these sentences? The vowels (a – e – i – o – u) are missing.

S*m tr**s v*ry h*rd t* l**rn h*s sp*ll*ngs.
Sam tries hard to learn his spellings.

D*d w*s *s*d t* c*m*ng h*m* *n th* tr**n.
Dad was used to coming home on the train.

1

2

PUZZLE 2 — Different sounds for oe (does) (goes) (shoes)

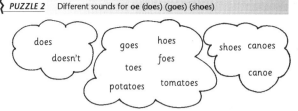

does   doesn't   goes   hoes   foes   toes   potatoes   tomatoes   shoes   canoes   canoe

Write some of these words into a pattern shape below. Some shapes may be the same.

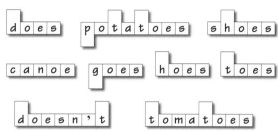

does   potatoes   shoes
canoe   goes   hoes   toes
doesn't   tomatoes

Begin at the top and find the eight words. The last letter of one word must always begin the next word.

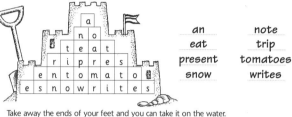

```
      a
    n o
  t e a t
  r i p r e s
e n t o m a t o
e s n o w r i t e s
```

an   note
eat   trip
present   tomatoes
snow   writes

Take away the ends of your feet and you can take it on the water.

n e c e t o a s o   →   canoe

PUZZLE 3 — Words beginning with the prefix be

Can you find the **be** words in the word square? They are all horizontal.

```
l o b e f o r e d r
u b e f b e g a n e
p b e i n g i n g s
b e n b e l o w s e
s e b e t w e e n d
b e l o n g i n d g
f o r b e n e a t h
a b e s i d e d o n
e b i b e h i n d e
o b e c a u s e s s
```

before
began
being
below
between
belong
beneath
beside
behind
because

Begin at the top and find the eight words. The last letter of one word must always begin the next word.

```
      t
    u b
  e g i n
e x t r u c
k e e p i c n i
c l i m b e c a m e
```

tub   begin
next   truck
keep   picnic
climb   became

This time write the eight words in the grid. The last letter of one word must always begin the next word.

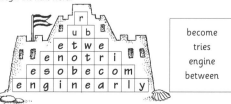

```
      r
    u b
  e t w e
e n o t r i
e s o b e c o m
e n g i n e a r l y
```

become   not
tries   early
engine   sob
between   rub

3

4

PUZZLE 4 — Vowel sound igh (night)

Finish the puzzle by adding the pattern **igh** and most times a **t**.

n
f
br
fl
fr
h
kn
l
m
r
th
ton
del

igh + t

night
fight
bright
flight
fright
high
knight
light
might
right
thigh
tonight
delight

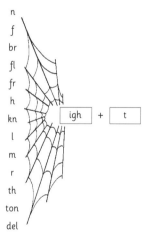

2

How many words do not end with the letter **t**?

Can you turn **cats** into **mice** by changing each word one letter at a time? There is a clue for each new word.

c a t s	
c a n s	another word for tins
c a n e	a stick to tie plants to
p a n e	glass in a window
m a n e	hair on a horse's neck
m i n e	it's not yours but ...
m i c e	small furry animals

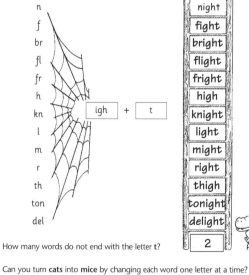

Begin with a silent **k** or a silent **w** to make words.

not	rite	reck	now	neel
knot	**write**	**wreck**	**know**	**kneel**

new	rap	nife	rote	nock
knew	**wrap**	**knife**	**wrote**	**knock**

In these words the letters **ph** make the sound of an **f**.
Which word matches the clue? Fill in the missing letters.

| trophy | sphere | graph | hyphen | phone | nephew |

s p **h e r e** it is round   p **h o n e** a mobile ...
g r a p **h** a chart   n e p h **e w** brother of niece
h y p h **e n** joins two words   t r **o p h y** the winner's prize

Can you finish the crosswords?

Across
1. used for cutting
3. Granny ... a pullover

Down
1. ... before entering
2. tests in school

Across
1. Lee ... a letter.
3. the day now

Down
1. part of your arm
2. opposite of full

Across
1. does up a parcel
3. a happening

Down
1. do it with a pen
2. opposite of stop

5

| change | danger | strange | orange | angel | anger |

Write each word into a pattern shape below.

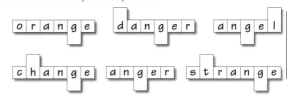

Use the words in the box to fill in the crossword.

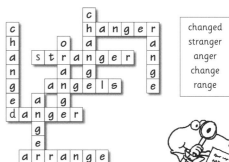

changed	hanger
stranger	angels
anger	orange
change	danger
range	arrange

Finish the spello-gram.

My first is in **on** but not in **in**.
My second is in **hard** but not in **hand**.
My third is in **sand** but not in **send**.
My fourth is in **pine** but not in **pipe**.
My fifth is in **wage** but not in **wake**.
My sixth is in **east** but not in **past**.   What fruit am I? | **orange** |

6

Arrange these two word groups into alphabetical order.

leave	while
such	much
gone	told
able	head
white	above

| able |
| **above gone** |
| **head leave** |
| **much such** |
| **told while** |
| **white** |

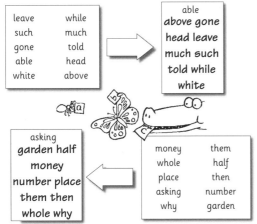

| asking |
| **garden half** |
| **money** |
| **number place** |
| **them then** |
| **whole why** |

money	them
whole	half
place	then
asking	number
why	garden

Arrange the words in alphabetical order in the correct column.

| flowers | pages | weeds | meat | story | lawn |
| cooking | words | biscuits | snails | titles | dinner |

Garden	**Books**	**Food**
flowers	pages	biscuits
lawn	story	cooking
snails	titles	dinner
weeds	words	meat

7

8

Write these words in their own **ough** sound box.

though	cough	rough
dough	**trough**	**tough enough**
although		

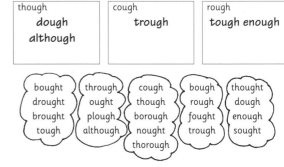

bought	through	cough	bough	thought
drought	ought	though	rough	dough
brought	plough	borough	fought	enough
tough	although	nought	trough	sought
		thorough		

thorough	ought	bough
borough	**bought brought**	**plough**
	fought nought	**drought**
	sought thought	

Which word needs a box of its own? | **through** |

Write the sounds of each word in a box.

brought | b | r | ough | t | fought | f | ough | t |
enough | e | n | ou | gh | drought | d | r | ough | t |
cough | c | ou | gh | though | th | ough |
thought | th | ough | t | rough | r | ou | gh |
ought | ough | t | trough | t | r | ou | gh |

Can you find the **al** words in the word square? They are all vertical.

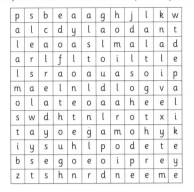

p	s	b	e	a	a	g	h	j	l	k	w
a	l	c	d	y	l	a	o	d	a	n	t
l	e	a	o	a	s	l	m	a	l	a	d
a	r	l	f	l	t	o	i	l	t	l	e
l	s	r	a	o	a	u	a	s	o	i	p
m	a	e	l	n	l	d	l	o	g	v	a
o	l	a	t	e	o	a	a	h	e	e	l
s	w	d	h	t	n	l	r	o	t	x	i
t	a	y	o	e	g	a	m	o	h	y	k
i	y	s	u	h	l	p	o	d	e	t	e
b	s	e	g	o	e	o	i	p	r	e	y
z	t	s	h	n	r	d	n	e	e	m	e

almost
always
already
although
alone
along
aloud
alarm
also
altogether
alive
alike

Begin at the top and find the eight words. The last letter of one word must always begin the next word.

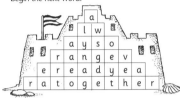

always   so
orange   ever
ready   year
rat   together

This time write the eight words in the grid. The last letter of one word must always begin the next word.

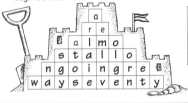

seventy	going
grew	area
ways	long
almost	tall

Make six **ever** and six **even** words.

n|ever| s|even| el|even| |ever|y
s|even|th cl|ever| for|ever| |even|t.
|ever|yone el|even|th cl|ever|ly s|even|ty

Beginning with **c**, take every second letter to make eleven **ever** or **even** words. Write the words in the finishing box.

clever seven forever
seventy cleverly never
seventh every event
eleventh everyone

How many words did you find? [   ]

Complete the words using the letters **on** or **un**.

u n d e r	o n c e	f r o n t
o n l y	L o n d o n	u n t i l
u p o n	u n c l e	p o n y

Write each **under** word into a pattern shape below. Some shapes may be the same.

understand   understood   underneath   underline

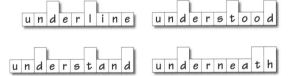

u n d e r l i n e   u n d e r s t o o d

u n d e r s t a n d   u n d e r n e a t h

Finish the puzzles by printing under each letter the one that comes before it in the alphabet. Use capital letters.

Which word is the opposite of back? front

Which word is the opposite of over? under

Can you add these words together?

Beginning with **a**, take every second letter and write the five words in the finishing box.

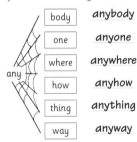

any
body → anybody
one → anyone
where → anywhere
how → anyhow
thing → anything
way → anyway

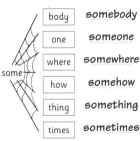

some
body → somebody
one → someone
where → somewhere
how → somehow
thing → something
times → sometimes

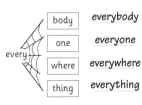

every
body → everybody
one → everyone
where → everywhere
thing → everything

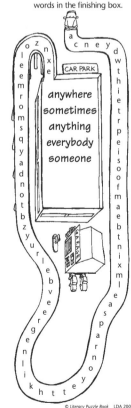

anywhere
sometimes
anything
everybody
someone

PUZZLE 13 Times and days

Can you find the times of the day and the days in the word square?
They are all horizontal.

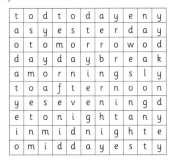

t	o	d	t	o	d	a	y	e	n	y
a	s	y	e	s	t	e	r	d	a	y
o	t	o	m	o	r	r	o	w	o	d
d	a	y	d	a	y	b	r	e	a	k
a	m	o	r	n	i	n	g	s	l	y
t	o	a	f	t	e	r	n	o	o	n
y	e	s	e	v	e	n	i	n	g	d
e	t	o	n	i	g	h	t	a	n	y
i	n	m	i	d	n	i	g	h	t	e
o	m	i	d	d	a	y	e	s	t	y

today
yesterday
tomorrow
daybreak
morning
afternoon
evening
tonight
midnight
midday

Write in the answers to finish the crossword.

3 letters day

4 letters year easy been

5 letters today white weeks irons

6 letters taking letter breeze

7 letters tonight teacake

8 letters earnings

10 letters thoughtful

PUZZLE 14 Words ending in **ring**

Write down the ten **ring** words hidden in the word square. The words go across and down.

r	s	a	d	m	i	r	i	n	g
i	c	c	a	r	o	n	g	e	d
n	o	b	d	u	r	i	n	g	s
o	r	o	k	d	e	n	t	l	e
f	i	r	o	d	a	r	i	n	g
f	n	i	b	a	c	k	r	e	d
i	g	n	s	c	a	r	i	n	g
r	m	g	l	a	r	i	n	g	l
i	e	t	s	l	i	n	g	r	i
n	b	c	s	o	n	e	y	o	z
g	u	p	a	n	g	e	s	t	e

admiring   firing
during   scoring
daring   boring
scaring   caring
glaring   tiring

Write out the coded words.

a	1
b	2
c	3
d	4
e	5
f	6
g	7
h	8
i	9
j	10
k	11
l	12
m	13
n	14
o	15
p	16
q	17
r	18
s	19
t	20
u	21
v	22
w	23
x	24
y	25
z	26

4 21 18 9 14 7 → d u r i n g — during

2 15 18 9 14 7 → b o r i n g — boring

3 1 18 9 14 7 → c a r i n g — caring

19 3 15 18 9 14 7 → s c o r i n g — scoring

4 1 18 9 14 7 → d a r i n g — daring

1 4 13 9 18 9 14 7 → a d m i r i n g — admiring

7 12 1 18 9 14 7 → g l a r i n g — glaring

6 9 18 9 14 7 → f i r i n g — firing

19 3 1 18 9 14 7 → s c a r i n g — scaring

20 9 18 9 14 7 → t i r i n g — tiring

PUZZLE 15 Letter patterns **oft** and **tch**

Finish the sums.

s + oft = soft

l + oft = loft

s + oft + en = soften

oft + en = often

s + oft + ly = softly

al + oft = aloft

Finish the puzzle.

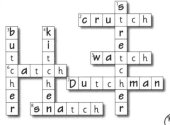

1. often used for carrying a sick person
2. you may need one if you break your leg
3. a person who sells meat
4. the room in the house used for cooking
5. usually worn on the wrist
6. Sam caught the first ball. Cathy will … the next one.
7. a man from the Netherlands
8. when you grab something quickly you …

Take away the opposite of **hard** and you are left with a teller of time.

h f c o a t t s w → watch

Take away **frequently** and you can cook a meal here.

t e e i n t h f k o c n → kitchen

PUZZLE 16 Double-letter words

Use the code to find out the words.

a	b	c	d	e	f	g	h	i	j	k	l	m
Z	Y	X	W	V	U	T	S	R	Q	P	O	N

n	o	p	q	r	s	t	u	v	w	x	y	z
M	L	K	J	I	H	G	F	E	D	C	B	A

Y V G G V I → better

H G R O O → still

S Z K K B → happy

W R U U V I V M G → different

H F W W V M O B → suddenly

H D R N N R M T → swimming

Y Z O O L L M → balloon

Use the words in the box to fill in the crossword.

happiness	rabbit
winner	bigger
better	manner
sudden	hidden
swimming	error

Can you decode these sentences? The double consonant letters are missing.

Rebe**a was a be**er swi**er than her bi**er brother.
Rebecca was a better swimmer than her bigger brother.

The shape of the blue ba**oon was sti** di**erent from the red one.
The shape of the blue balloon was still different from the red one.

Su**enly, E**ie sto**ed crying and was ha**y again.
Suddenly, Ellie stopped crying and was happy again.

Finish the pattern. We add **er** when comparing two and **est** for more than two.

	+ er	+ est
fast	faster	fastest
great	greater	greatest
near	nearer	nearest
round	rounder	roundest
small	smaller	smallest
loud	louder	loudest
young	younger	youngest

Now try these tricky ones. The base word changes.

little	less	least
good	better	best
many	more	most
bad	worse	worst

These numbers represent letters. Can you write the words?

1	2	3	4	5
s	t	a	l	e

5	3	1	2		4	3	1	2
e	a	s	t		l	a	s	t

4	5	1	1		2	3	4	5
l	e	s	s		t	a	l	e

1	5	4	4		1	5	3	2
s	e	l	l		s	e	a	t

1	2	5	3	4		4	5	3	1	2
s	t	e	a	l		l	e	a	s	t

Which word is a story?   tale

---

inside	outside	beside	sideways
without	outdoors	outline	outwards

Write each word into a pattern shape below.

i n s i d e   o u t l i n e   w i t h o u t

b e s i d e   o u t s i d e   s i d e w a y s

o u t w a r d s   o u t d o o r s

Now use some of the words to describe the pictures.

beside   **outdoors**   **outside**

inside   **outline**   **sideways**

Can you decode these sentences? The vowels (a – e – i – o – u) are missing.

S*m* ch*ldr*n w*r* *ns*de *nd *th*rs w*r* **ts*d*.
Some children were inside and others were outside.

T*d*y **r t**ch*r s**d w* c**ld pl*y **td**rs.
Today our teacher said we could play outdoors.

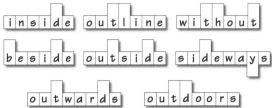

---

board	cross	head	lone	long	loud
mount	round	sleep	wake	while	woke

Write each word into a pattern shape below. Some shapes may be the same.

Then write each new word beginning with an **a**.

b o a r d   aboard   h e a d   ahead

c r o s s   across   l o n g   along

l o n e   alone   m o u n t   amount

s l e e p   asleep   w a k e   awake

r o u n d   around   w h i l e   awhile

l o u d   aloud   w o k e   awoke

Can you decode these sentences? The vowels (a – e – i – o – u) are missing.

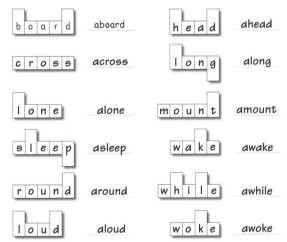

R*j w**t*d *r**nd th* c*rn*r *nt*l h*s fr**nd c*m* *l*ng.
Raj waited around the corner until his friend came along.

Th* sch**l f*t* r**s*d th* *m**nt *f £500 f*r * n*w c*mp*t*r.
The school fete raised the amount of £500 for a new computer.

Find the **ath**, **eth** and **oth** words in the word square. They are all vertical.

e	l	y	s	o	r	c	f	b	i	t
m	g	e	o	f	o	a	i	i	b	o
o	a	t	t	a	b	l	l	g	o	f
t	r	o	h	t	r	t	c	a	t	a
h	a	g	e	h	o	o	l	t	b	t
e	t	e	r	p	t	g	o	h	o	h
r	h	t	l	a	h	e	t	e	t	e
e	e	h	o	t	e	t	h	r	h	r
d	r	e	b	h	r	h	e	e	o	a
s	e	r	o	e	i	e	s	f	r	n
a	y	n	t	p	s	r	t	d	g	e

mother
rather
together
other
path
brother
altogether
clothes
gather
both
father

Write in the answers to finish the crossword.

3 letters ape
4 letters both help path
5 letters above other truth froth tasty
6 letters trench bother
7 letters clothes scamper
8 letters takeaway
10 letters altogether

PUZZLE 21 Animals

Change one letter in each word to spell the name of an animal.

big	deck	for	rut	cot	worse
pig	duck	fox	rat	cat	horse

Find the animals in the word square. They are all horizontal.

p	u	d	p	u	p	p	i	e	s	s		puppies
a	n	g	l	l	i	o	n	e	s	t		lion
s	a	l	e	o	p	a	r	d	e	d		leopard
j	i	r	a	g	i	r	a	f	f	e		giraffe
c	a	k	i	t	t	e	n	s	n	y		kittens
d	o	n	t	m	o	n	k	e	y	y		monkey
a	r	r	e	i	n	d	e	e	r	k		reindeer
h	a	r	h	o	r	s	e	t	o	e		horse
c	o	t	i	g	e	r	e	s	e	n		tiger
a	d	o	n	k	e	y	t	i	o	n		donkey

Use the animal words in the box to fill in the crossword.

animals	kitten
giraffe	tiger
monkey	horse
leopard	dog

Take away the parent of a foal and you are left with a tall animal.

r s f h a r g f o i e e   **giraffe**

21

~~~~ 22

PUZZLE 22 Contractions

Sort out the jumbled letters into two words. Then turn them into contractions. Do not forget the apostrophe.

tonidd	=	didn't		rtonae	=	aren't
nacton	=	can't		tonsaw	=	wasn't
dtono	=	don't		adtonh	=	hadn't
stonha	=	hasn't		vetonha	=	haven't
stoni	=	isn't		retonwe	=	weren't
cuotonld	=	couldn't		wtonuodl	=	wouldn't
houtonsdl	=	shouldn't		siti	=	it's
siereht	=	there's		hatsit	=	that's
erehis	=	here's		reayuo	=	you're
mIa	=	I'm		avehI	=	I've

Finish the crossword by using the contraction of each clue. Use a separate square for each apostrophe.

Across
2. would not
6. is not
7. I am
8. did not
9. she will

Down
1. do not
3. does not
4. that is
5. cannot
7. I will

PUZZLE 23 Letter pattern ound

Finish the **ound** puzzle.

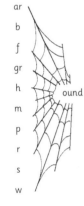

ar
b
f
gr
h
m
p
r
s
w

ound

around			
bound	+	ing	=	bounding
found	+	ed	=	founded
ground	+	ed	=	grounded
hound	+	s	=	hounds
mound	+	s	=	mounds
pound	+	ed	=	pounded
round	+	er	=	rounder
sound	+	ing	=	sounding
wound			

Can you finish the rhyming crossword?

Across
1. rhymes with sound
3. rhymes with bought
6. rhymes with train
7. rhymes with page
9. rhymes with rough
10. rhymes with mound

Down
2. rhymes with brown
4. rhymes with caught
5. rhymes with tree
7. rhymes with dish
8. rhymes with mutter

Other answers possible

23

~~~ 24

PUZZLE 24 Some ear words

Can you find the **ear** words?

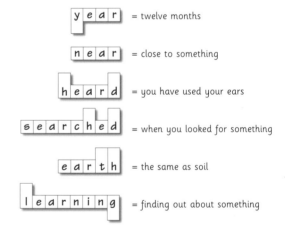

y e a r = twelve months

n e a r = close to something

h e a r d = you have used your ears

s e a r c h e d = when you looked for something

e a r t h = the same as soil

l e a r n i n g = finding out about something

Can you decode these sentences? The vowels (a – e – i – o – u) are missing.

N*xt y**r w* w*ll b* tr*nsf*rr*ng t* **r n*w sch**l.
Next year we will be transferring to our new school.

*t **r n*w sch**l w* w*ll b*g*n t* l*rn Fr*nch.
At our new school we will begin to learn French.

Th* s**rch f*r th* l*st d*g h*d l*st*d tw* d*ys.
The search for the lost dog had lasted two days.

Th* s**rch*rs f**nd th* d*g wh*n th*y h**rd *ts cr**s f*r h*lp.
The searchers found the dog when they heard its cries for help.

Can you find the members of the family? The words are all horizontal.

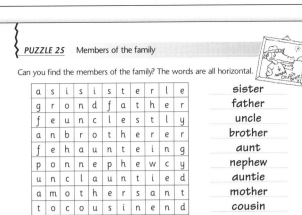

a	s	i	s	i	s	t	e	r	l	e
g	r	o	n	d	f	a	t	h	e	r
f	e	u	n	c	l	e	s	t	l	y
a	n	b	r	o	t	h	e	r	e	r
f	e	h	a	u	n	t	e	i	n	g
p	o	n	n	e	p	h	e	w	c	y
u	n	c	l	a	u	n	t	i	e	d
a	m	o	t	h	e	r	s	a	n	t
t	o	c	o	u	s	i	n	e	n	d
b	a	b	b	a	b	y	l	t	e	x
a	c	h	i	l	d	r	e	n	e	l
s	i	s	b	e	n	i	e	c	e	r

sister
father
uncle
brother
aunt
nephew
auntie
mother
cousin
baby
children
niece

Begin at the top and find the eight words. The last letter of one word must always begin the next word.

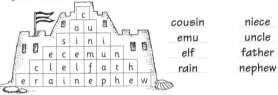

cousin   niece
emu   uncle
elf   father
rain   nephew

This time write the eight words in the grid. The last letter of one word must always begin the next word.

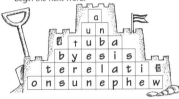

aunt   sister
sun   yes
baby   tub
relations   nephew

Join each word in the box with a word below to make compound words.
Only use each word once.

after	day	news	for	bed	out
birth	card	post	fire	dish	door

dishcloth   **day** light   **after**noon
outside   **card**board   **birth**day
doorknob   **bed**room   **news**paper
postbox   **for**ward   **fire**place

Use each consonant once to finish some of the compound words above.

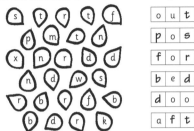

o	u	t	s	i	d	e
p	o	s	t	b	o	x
f	o	r	w	a	r	d
b	e	d	r	o	o	m
d	o	o	r	k	n	o	b
a	f	t	e	r	n	o	o	n

The beginning words have the wrong endings. Can you sort them out?

dish	noon		dish	cloth		flower	ball		**flower**	**bed**
in	light		**in**	**side**		after	paper		**after**	**noon**
snow	case		**snow**	**ball**		head	side		**head**	**light**
news	cloth		**news**	**paper**		stair	bed		**stair**	**case**

Write each **ure** word and draw a line to its meaning.

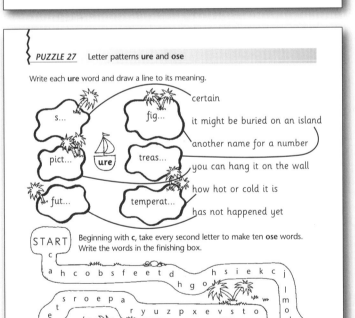

s...
fig...
pict...
treas...
fut...
temperat...

ure

certain
it might be buried on an island
another name for a number
you can hang it on the wall
how hot or cold it is
has not happened yet

START
Beginning with **c**, take every second letter to make ten **ose** words. Write the words in the finishing box.

chose those closer
suppose purpose
rosebud closely
arose close whose

How many words did you find?

Take a word from the box and write it beside its opposite in the lake.

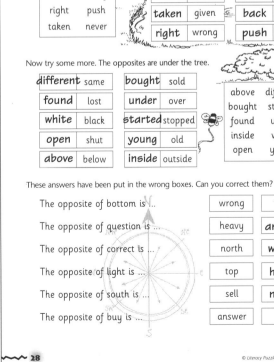

after	back
here	last
little	many
right	push
taken	never

never always   **here** there
many few   **after** before
little big   **last** first
taken given   **back** front
right wrong   **push** pull

Now try some more. The opposites are under the tree.

different same   **bought** sold
found lost   **under** over
white black   **started** stopped
open shut   **young** old
above below   **inside** outside

above	different
bought	started
found	under
inside	white
open	young

These answers have been put in the wrong boxes. Can you correct them?

The opposite of bottom is ...	wrong	**top**
The opposite of question is ...	heavy	**answer**
The opposite of correct is ...	north	**wrong**
The opposite of light is ...	top	**heavy**
The opposite of south is ...	sell	**north**
The opposite of buy is ...	answer	**sell**

Make six **port** words and six **light** words.

s	port		f	light		s	light	ly		im	port	ant
re	port		de	light			port	rait			light	ning
	light	ing		port	hole		port	able		light	en

Can you find the two hidden words? Take every second letter in a clockwise direction. Go around the lifebelt twice and write the words in the centre.

Start here.

important
slightly

© Literacy Puzzle Book   LDA 2001

29

Find the smaller words in each long word. Can you find them all?

heart	he a hear ear art	5
thinking	thin think in ink inking king kin in	8
shown	show ho how ow own	5
disappear	is sap a appear pea pear ear a	8
everywhere	every eve ever very where here he her	8
discovery	disc disco is cove cover over very	7
important	imp import port or tan a an ant	8
something	so me some met thin thing in	7
interesting	in interest inter rest resting sting tin in	8
stranger	strange ran rang range ranger a an anger	8

Finish the puzzles by printing under each letter the one that comes before it in the alphabet. Use capital letters.

Which word means shines with steady light?   glows

Which word means say something loudly?   shout

30

© Literacy Puzzle Book   LDA 2001

Beginning with **w**, take every second letter to make twelve **wor** words. Write the words in the finishing box.

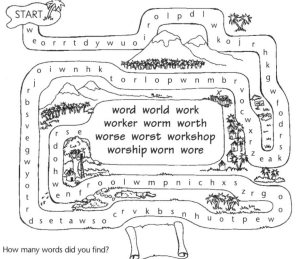

word world work
worker worm worth
worse worst workshop
worship worn wore

How many words did you find?

Subtract a letter from each word in the first column. The clues will help you to find the new word. Use the subtracted letters to find the opposite of **best**.

Words	Clues	Word	Letter
town	a very heavy weight	ton	w
point	a measure of liquid	pint	o
work	used for cooking	wok	r
worse	Jenny ... her black boots	wore	s
trip	a tear in your coat	rip	t

The opposite of **best** is   worst

© Literacy Puzzle Book   LDA 2001

31

Make four **ape**, four **wind** and four **end** words.

gr	ape	s		wind	ow	fri	end	s		p	ape	er
sp	end	s	sh	ape	s		wind	ing	bl	end	s
	wind	mill	fri	end	ly	esc	ape	d		wind	y

Look at the letters in each shape and finish the puzzle.

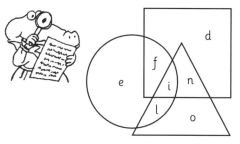

Which letter appears only in the circle?	e
Which two letters appear in the square and the triangle?	n i
Which letter appears only in the square?	d
What word can you spell with these four letters?	dine
Which letter appears in all three shapes?	i
What word can you make with the four letters in the square?	find
What two letters do you need to turn this word into **friend**?	r e
Can you make two words with the letters in the circle?	file life
What animal can you make with the four letters in the triangle?	lion

© Literacy Puzzle Book   LDA 2001

32

PUZZLE 33 Singulars and plurals

Finish the patterns.

one	more than one
animal	animals
eye	eyes
house	houses
place	places

one	more than one
box	boxes
glass	glasses
bush	bushes
watch	watches

one	more than one
fly	flies
spy	spies
lady	ladies
baby	babies

one	more than one
half	halves
calf	calves
knife	knives
wife	wives

one	more than one
echo	echoes
hero	heroes
potato	potatoes
tomato	tomatoes

Be careful with these patterns.

one	more than one
child	children
foot	feet
tooth	teeth
mouse	mice

one	more than one
deer	deer
sheep	sheep
trout	trout
cod	cod

Finish the spello-gram.

My first is in **calf** but not in **half**.
My second is in **halves** but not in **calves**.
My third is in **write** but not in **wrote**.
My fourth is in **flies** but not in **fries**.
My fifth is in **cod** but not in **cot**.
My sixth is in **deer** but not in **deep**.
My seventh is in **one** but not in **won**.
My eighth is in **nice** but not in **mice**.

Who are we? | children |

33

PUZZLE 34 Homophones

These words have the same sound but different spellings.

a large animal | b e a r |
uncovered | b a r e |

a colour | b l u e |
the wind ... | b l e w |

a ... of cattle | h e r d |
listened | h e a r d |

the opposite of yes | n o |
I ... the way | k n o w |

certain | s u r e |
the coastline | s h o r e |

sports day was ... | g r e a t |
make tiny pieces | g r a t e |

not wrong | r i g h t |
use a pen to ... | w r i t e |

he ... the ball | t h r e w |
end to end | t h r o u g h |

have on as clothing | w e a r |
to what place | w h e r e |

you can dig one | h o l e |
all of something | w h o l e |

Cross out all the letters that appear twice in each grid below.
Then rearrange the remaining letters to give the two homophones.

e	f	i	a	z	b
y	t	v	l	n	x
c	k	p	j	d	s
x	h	a	s	y	o
z	l	b	i	k	c
d	v	j	r	p	f

c	i	a	s	d	o
g	f	l	i	y	v
m	h	z	w	p	b
b	n	u	g	v	z
d	s	y	p	c	t
f	r	u	a	m	l

Answer **throne**   Answer **thrown**

34

PUZZLE 35 Some eye and lad words

Write in six **eye** and six **lad** words.

eye	s		lad	y		lad	ies		eye	ball
g	lad		eye	lid		eye	brow		g	lad	ly
eye	lash		b	lad	e		eye	sight		sa	lad

Four of these words are hidden in the circle below. Take every second letter and go clockwise around the eye twice. Write the words in the centre.

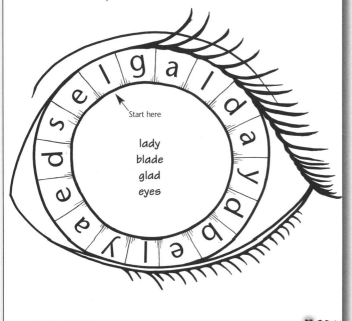

Start here

lady
blade
glad
eyes

35

PUZZLE 36 Parents and young, and creatures and their homes

Decode each jumbled young animal and use it to finish the clues below.

tnetki	bmla	lickudgn	idk	gnilosg	glipet
kitten	lamb	duckling	kid	gosling	piglet
lepodta	lafc	ucb	loaf	gycten	upp
tadpole	calf	cub	foal	cygnet	pup

A young dog is called a | pup |
A young cow is called a | calf |
A young sheep is called a | lamb |
A young swan is called a | cygnet |
A young goose is called a | gosling |
A young goat is called a | kid |

A young bear is called a | cub |
A young duck is called a | duckling |
A young frog is called a | tadpole |
A young horse is called a | foal |
A young pig is called a | piglet |
A young cat is called a | kitten |

These answers have been put in the wrong boxes. Can you correct them?

The home of a lion is called a ...
A bee lives in a ...
The home of a bird is called a ...
A dog lives in a ...
The home of a horse is called a ...
The home of a tame rabbit is called a ...
A wild rabbit lives in a ...
The home of a spider is called a ...
The home of a hare is called a ...
A snail lives in a ...

hutch	den
den	hive
web	nest
nest	kennel
burrow	stable
kennel	hutch
stable	burrow
form	web
shell	form
hive	shell

36

57

Decode each word and use it to finish the clues below.

a	b	c	d	e	f	g	h	i	j	k	l	m
Z	Y	X	W	V	U	T	S	R	Q	P	O	N
n	o	p	q	r	s	t	u	v	w	x	y	z
M	L	K	J	I	H	G	F	E	D	C	B	A

Y Z O V → b a l e   S V I W → h e r d   X I V D → c r e w   U O L X P → f l o c k

T Z T T O V → g a g g l e   X S V H G → c h e s t   H D Z I N → s w a r m

H X S L L O → s c h o o l   Y F M X S → b u n c h   G I L L K → t r o o p

O R G G V I → l i t t e r   Y L F J F V G → b o u q u e t

a [crew] of sailors   a [bouquet] of flowers
a [flock] of birds   a [bunch] of grapes
a [gaggle] of geese   a [chest] of drawers
a [herd] of cattle   a [school] of whales
a [litter] of pups   a [swarm] of bees
a [bale] of wool   a [troop] of monkeys

Take away the ship's crew and you are left with the fruit.

r i p s a r s a s g l e o   [grapes]

Take away the young dogs and you have somewhere to put your clothes.

s p a u p d e r p s i w r e   [drawers]

Decode each jumbled word and use it to finish the clues below.

korc	wol	blam	heratef	linsa	nebo
rock	owl	lamb	feather	snail	bone
suome	ebe	reah	stohg	rebmuccu	nilo
mouse	bee	hare	ghost	cucumber	lion

as brave as a ... [lion]   as slow as a ... [snail]
as busy as a ... [bee]   as wise as an ... [owl]
as fast as a ... [hare]   as white as a ... [sheet]
as cool as a ... [cucumber]   as dry as a ... [bone]
as gentle as a ... [lamb]   as light as a ... [feather]
as quiet as a ... [mouse]   as steady as a ... [rock]

Who does what? The answers are all wrong. Can you correct them?

A person who mends pipes and taps is a ...	florist	plumber
A person who looks after our teeth is a ...	jockey	dentist
A person who looks after our eyes is an ...	pilot	optician
A person who grows plants is a ...	plumber	gardener
A person who rides a race horse is a ...	butcher	jockey
A person who flies an aeroplane is a ...	optician	pilot
A person who makes us laugh at the circus is a ...	gardener	clown
A person who sells flowers is a ...	artist	florist
A person who sells meat is a ...	dentist	butcher
A person who paints pictures is an ...	clown	artist

Each sentence is wrong. Can you write the correct animal in the boxes?

a **pig** neighs and gallops   [horse]
a **horse** barks and runs   [dog]
a **mouse** brays and trots   [donkey]
a **duck** roars and prowls   [lion]
a **dog** squeaks and scampers   [mouse]
a **lion** talks and walks   [person]

a **bird** grunts and trots   [pig]
a **hen** whistles and flies   [bird]
a **donkey** quacks and waddles   [duck]
a **turkey** cackles and struts   [hen]
a **elephant** gobbles and struts [turkey]
an **person** trumpets and ambles [elephant]

Use each vowel below to finish the animals.

p	i	g		
d	o	g		
b	i	r	d	
d	u	c	k	
l	i	o	n	
m	o	u	s	e
h	o	r	s	e
d	o	n	k	e	y
t	u	r	k	e	y
e	l	e	p	h	a	n	t

Decode each jumbled word and use it to finish the proverbs below.

reven	lemi	tonreha	tarped	edinde	enin
never	mile	another	parted	indeed	nine
nidm	kilea	pela	lewl	tegrheot	wens
mind	alike	leap	well	together	news

A fool and his money are soon ... [parted]
A friend in need is a friend ... [indeed]
All's well that ends ... [well]
A miss is as good as a ... [mile]
A stitch in time saves ... [nine]
Better late than ... [never]

Birds of a feather flock ... [together]
Great minds think ... [alike]
Look before you ... [leap]
No news is good ... [news]
One good turn deserves ... [another]
Out of sight, out of ... [mind]

Can you decode these proverbs? Every word is jumbled.

A tichst ni meti avess enin.   sdriB fo a thefear lfokc otertheg.
A stitch in time saves nine.   **Birds of a feather flock together.**

A endirf ni deen si a firdne nedide. tteBer tale anth veern.
A friend in need is a friend indeed. **Better late than never.**

Use these words to finish the puzzles below.

painting	modern	south	army	fish	month
nephew	leg	up	April	mother	woman

boy is to man as girl is to ...   **woman**

father is to son as ... is to daughter   **mother**

high is to low as ... is to down   **up**

wrist is to arm as ankle is to ...   **leg**

north is to ... as east is to west   **south**

uncle is to ... as aunt is to niece   **nephew**

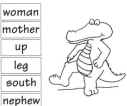

wing is to bird as fin is to ...   **fish**

June is to July as ... is to May   **April**

day is to week as ... is to year   **month**

rich is to poor as ancient is to ...   **modern**

soldier is to ... as sailor is to navy   **army**

artist is to ... as author is to writing   **painting**

Begin at the top and find the eight words. The last letter of one word must always begin the next word.

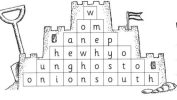

woman   nephew
why   young
ghost   too
onions   south

© Literacy Puzzle Book   LDA 2001   41

Can you answer the puzzles?

What day comes before Tuesday?   Monday

What day comes after Saturday?   Sunday

What day is between Tuesday and Thursday?   Wednesday

Write the word for the number of days in a week.   seven

What day is two days before Sunday?   Friday

What day is between Monday and Wednesday?   Tuesday

What day is between Friday and Sunday?   Saturday

What is the abbreviation for Wednesday?   Wed.

How many days are there in a fortnight?   fourteen

How many days start with the letter 'T'?   two

What day is two days after Tuesday?   Thursday

How many days are there in a leap year?   366

Finish the sentences. Each dash stands for a letter.

Last T<u>hurs</u> day it was very hot, but F <u>ri</u> day was cold and wet.

We will be in Scotland from next Wed<u>nes</u> day to Sat<u>ur</u> day.

This year my birthday is on a M<u>on</u> day.

Can you come over to my house next T<u>ues</u> day?

42   © Literacy Puzzle Book   LDA 2001

What month am I?

Abbreviations of the months begin with capital letters and end with full stops.
May, June and **July** are not abbreviated.

Jan.	January	**July**	July
Feb.	February	**Aug.**	August
Mar.	March	**Sept.**	September
Apr.	April	**Oct.**	October
May	May	**Nov.**	November
June	June	**Dec.**	December

Finish the spello-gram.

What month am I?

My first letter is in **fit** but not in **bit**.
My second letter is in **well** but not in **wall**.
My third letter is in **tube** but not in **tune**.
My fourth letter is in **read** but not in **bead**.
My fifth letter is in **aunt** but not in **ant**.
My sixth letter is in **lake** but not in **like**.
My seventh letter is in **crown** but not in **clown**.
My eighth letter is in **by** but not in **be**.
I am the month of **February**.

Fill in the missing words.

Thirty days hath S**eptember**, A**pril**, J**une** and N**ovember**.
All the rest have **31**, excepting F**ebruary** all alone, which
has but **28** days clear, and **29** in each leap year.

© Literacy Puzzle Book   LDA 2001   43

Finish the pattern.

1	one	1st	11	eleven	11th
2	two	2nd	12	twelve	12th
3	three	3rd	13	thirteen	13th
4	four	4th	14	fourteen	14th
5	five	5th	15	fifteen	15th
6	six	6th	16	sixteen	16th
7	seven	7th	17	seventeen	17th
8	eight	8th	18	eighteen	18th
9	nine	9th	19	nineteen	19th
10	ten	10th	20	twenty	20th

Can you do these number puzzles? Write your answers in words.

What comes between twelve and fourteen?   thirteen

How many less than nineteen is ten?   nine

Take eight from nine and add eleven.   twelve

Add five, seven and eight.   twenty

What is half of two less than sixteen?   seven

Multiply four by four.   sixteen

How many articles in a dozen?   twelve

Divide eighteen by six.   three

What is the second even number after ten?   fourteen

What is the third odd number after ten?   fifteen

44   © Literacy Puzzle Book   LDA 2001

PUZZLE 45 Numbers twenty to one hundred

These answers have been put in the wrong boxes. Can you correct them?

What is nine more than twenty?	88	29
What is 99 in words?	29	ninety-nine
What comes between sixty-nine and seventy-one?	59	70
Add twenty-four and twelve.	30	36
Multiply six by eight.	70	48
What number comes just before sixty?	24	59
What is eleven more than seventy-seven?	36	88
How many is two dozen?	40	24
Take twenty from fifty.	100	30
What number comes next after thirty-nine?	89	40
What is two before ninety-one?	48	89
How many is a century?	ninety-nine	100

Which numbers are we mixing?

t y e w n	d e r n u d	y t r i h
twenty	hundred	thirty

o y t r	e i y n t	n e v t e y
forty	ninety	seventy

t h g i y	x y i t	i y t f
eighty	sixty	fifty

PUZZLE 46 Colours

Which colours are we mixing?

mix yellow and [blue] to make green

mix blue and [red] to make purple

mix red and [yellow] to make orange

mix black and [white] to make grey

mix blue and red to make [purple]

mix blue and yellow to make [green]

mix black and white to make [grey]

mix red and yellow to make [orange]

mix red and white to make [pink]

mix red and green to make [brown]

Cross out all the letters that appear twice in each grid below. Then rearrange the remaining letters to give the names of two colours.

c	u	a	o	k	e
f	l	t	h	r	v
m	b	p	f	o	d
e	v	y	a	g	h
t	n	r	l	u	c
d	y	b	i	g	m

d	b	w	u	k	e
s	o	z	f	x	j
n	p	h	y	c	s
j	v	x	y	a	z
f	c	r	b	u	p
h	w	k	g	d	v

Answer   pink   Answer   orange

PUZZLE 47 My body

Name and draw a line to the parts of the body.

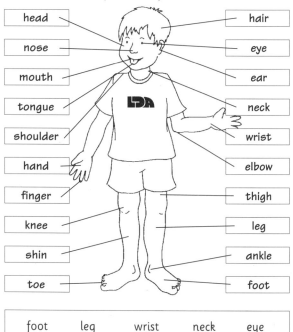

head		hair
nose		eye
mouth		ear
tongue		neck
shoulder		wrist
hand		elbow
finger		thigh
knee		leg
shin		ankle
toe		foot

foot	leg	wrist	neck	eye
toe	knee	hand	mouth	nose
head	tongue	shoulder	finger	shin
hair	ear	elbow	thigh	ankle

PUZZLE 48 Our language

Sometimes words in our language have the same spelling but different sounds and meanings. These words are called heteronyms.

Finish these sentences by using the word pairs.

wound	wound	produce	produce	refuse	refuse
present	present	row	row	minute	minute
close	close	wind	wind	tear	tear

When Sara saw the **tear** in her new coat she shed a **tear**.

The tables were too **close** for him to **close** the door.

The bandage was **wound** around the **wound** to stop it bleeding.

The tip was so full that the Council had to **refuse** more **refuse**.

The **wind** was so strong the sailors had to **wind** in the sails.

The farmer worked hard to **produce** as much **produce** as possible.

The children were ready to **present** the headteacher with her leaving **present**.

Every **minute** there seemed to be a **minute** musical sound from the computer.

There was a **row** among the crew about the best way to **row**.

Here are some more funny ones to answer.

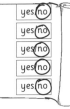

Is a kiwifruit a bird?	yes (no)
Do you have ham in hamburgers?	yes (no)
Are boxing rings round?	yes (no)
One tooth, two teeth. Is the plural of booth, beeth?	yes (no)
One goose, two geese. Is the plural of moose, meese?	yes (no)